For the Children

"Look at me, you young
folks. I just wrote a few
words in poetry about our
nation. I received the Order
of Canada. Whoopee, hot
dog, *may katu waltasi kisi
kelulnoq* (it feels good that I
can speak to you). Amen to
that. *Ta'ho'*."

—Rita Joe

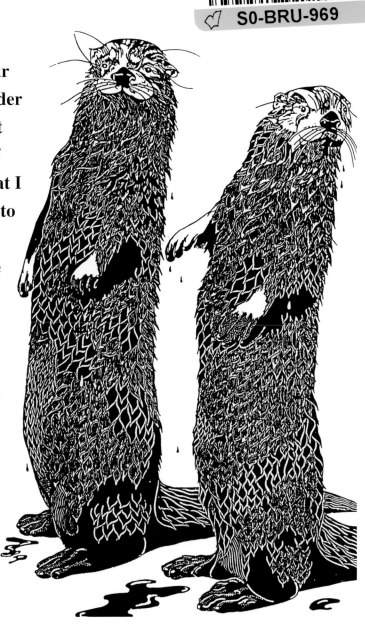

OTTERS

KESTREL

Rita Joe
For the Children

WITH WOODCUTS BY

Burland Murphy

Breton Books

Editor: Ronald Caplan
Production Assistance: Bonnie Thompson
    James Fader, Fader Communications

Editor's Note: Rita Joe died in March 2007. The poems in *For the Children* are a selection of published and unpublished poetry. We have decided to respect the Mi'kmaq words as she left them. She consistently used the Smith-Francis way of writing Mi'kmaw, which was developed by Bernard Francis and Douglas Smith in 1974, and in 1980 accepted as the official orthography of the Mi'kmaw Nation by the Grand Council. With the exception in this book: Rita Joe sometimes uses a hyphen (-) where in Smith-Francis it would not be used. For example, on page 28 she writes *Plo'qan-jij*. It could be written *Ploqan ji'j*, but as Rita Joe wrote it, it emphasizes the *ji'j*, the diminutive—which really is the point of the care and tenderness expressed by the entire poem. And so we have let it remain *Plo'qan-jij*. Overall, our goal has been to respect the words as Rita Joe left them to us. Where the Mi'kmaq words are translated, the translation is as found in her manuscripts or her printed poems. And in the one case where there is no translation—in the poem called "When I Am Gone"—we have left *Pe'kwam-uk-sin* untranslated, as she did. And we have left the hyphens in, which make us say the words slowly, contributing to the rhythm of that wonderful poem. We are grateful to Ann Joe, Rita's literary heir, and to Frances Sylliboy—two of Rita Joe's daughters—for their help and trust.

We acknowledge the support of the
Canada Council for the Arts for our publishing program.

Canada Council   Conseil des Arts
for the Arts   du Canada

We also acknowledge support from Cultural Affairs,
Nova Scotia Department of Tourism, Culture and Heritage.

NOVA SCOTIA
Tourism, Culture and Heritage

We acknowledge the financial support of the Government of Canada through the Book Publishing
Industry Development Program (BPIDP) for our publishing activities.

Canadä

Library and Archives Canada Cataloguing in Publication

Joe, Rita, 1932-2007
    For the children / Rita Joe ; with woodcuts by Burland Murphy ; editor,
Ronald Caplan.
Poems.
ISBN 978-1-895415-98-8
    I. Murphy, Burland, 1948- II. Caplan, Ronald, 1942- III. Title.
PS8569.O265F67 2008   C811'.54   C2008-901383-2

Contents

Woodcuts

There Is Life Everywhere

THE EVER-MOVING LEAVES of a poplar tree lessened my anxiety as I walked through the woods trying to make my mind work on a particular task I was worried about. The ever-moving leaves I touched with care, all the while talking to the tree. "Help me," I said. There is no help from anywhere, the moving story I want to share. There is a belief that all trees, rocks, anything that grows is alive, helps us in a way that no man can ever perceive, let alone even imagine. I am a Mi'kmaw woman who has lived a long time and know which is true and not true—you only try if you do not believe—I did, that is why my belief is so convincing to myself. There was a time when I was a little girl, my mother and father had both died and [I was] living at yet another foster home which was far away from a native community. The nearest neighbours were non-native and their children never went near our house, though I went to their school and got along with everybody, they still did not go near our home. It was at this time I was so lonely and wanted to play with other children my age which was twelve at the time. I began to experience unusual happiness when I lay on the ground near a brook just a few metres from our yard. At first I lay

For the Children   7

listening to the water; it seemed to be speaking to me with a comforting tone, a lullaby at times. Finally I moved my playhouse near it to be sure I never missed the comfort from it. Then I developed a friendship with a tree near the brook. The tree was just there, I touched the outside bark, the leaves I did not tear but caressed. A comforting feeling spread over me like warmth, a feeling you cannot experience unless you believe. That belief came when I was saddest. The sadness did not return after I knew that comfortable unity I shared with all living animals, birds, even the well I drew the water from. I talked to every bird I saw, the trees received the most hugs. Even today, others do not know the unconditional freedom I have experienced from the knowledge of knowing that this is possible. Try it and see. There is life everywhere, treat it as it is, it will not let you down.

—Rita Joe
Eskasoni

GOLDEN PLOVER

Keskmsi'

At age seven
I go to school
The teacher is talking
I do not understand much of what he says
So my stubby pencil makes contact
With a scrap of paper
I print small words,
The ones I know,
I try to put them in order.

"Bring that paper here," the teacher yells.
Timidly I walk, my knees trembling
I hand him the paper.
His eyes widen, "Where did you find these?"
I point at myself, my head, my heart,
The fear lessening.
He reads my first poem,
A jumble of words
"Kes-km-si' na"

I've caught up with myself,
That is why I am here
Poetry is my tool,
I create as I go

"*Kes-km-si' na,*" I tell you now.
Maybe tomorrow I will leave you,
Remember my stubby pencil,
and you too may "do."
Na kes-km-sit-isk naki'l elt.
You too will be ahead of yourself.

Keskmsi' means "ahead of myself"

A Mi'kmaw Cure-all for Ingrown Toenail

I have a comical story for ingrown toenail
I want to share with everybody
The person I love and admire is a friend
This is her cure-all for an elderly problem
She bought rubber boots one size larger
And put salted water above the toe
Then wore the boots all day
When evening came the cut was easy
The ingrown problem much better.
I laughed when I heard the story
It is because I have the same tender distress
So I might try the Mi'kmaw cure-all
The boots are there, just add the salted water
And laugh away the pesky sore
I'm even thinking of bottling for later use.

When I Was Small

When I was small
I used to help my father
Make axe handles.
Coming home from the wood with a bundle
Of *maskwi*, *snawey*, *aqmoq*,
My father would chip away,
Carving with a crooked knife,
Until a well-made handle appeared,
Ready to be sandpapered
By my brother.

When it was finished
We started another,
Sometimes working through the night
With me holding a lighted shaving
To light their way
When our kerosene lamp ran dry.

Then in the morning
My mother would be happy
That there would be food today
When my father sold our work.

The Road to Foster Home

Why is Dad hanging onto a fencepost?
Why did Grandmother fall down when the Chief spoke?
Why doesn't my sister Annabel answer my questions?

I am five years old
There are many things I do not understand
Like being taken to Grandmother's house
Then back to our house
Where there is a lot of food on the table
I eat some cakes
Later I am carried by my father
To view Mother in a long box

She is sleeping, they say
But she usually awakens when I call
She is so cold, "Cover her with a blanket, Dad."
He turns away, to face the wall

Finally they put the box in the ground
I hold somebody's hand

Grandma and Dad are hollering at each other
Dad wins the battle
We go away to some other place by train
It rocks back and forth, the wheels clatter

For the Children

We arrive at the first foster home
If Dad can help it
There will be many more

I Was That Kid

I used to walk into any house in Millbrook N.S.
A fresh piece of bannock would be handed to me
"Eat this, go out to play"
There was this one house, the mom and dad
And their only child.
I was like a fixture there. When the table was set
I'd be the first to eat.
Finally one day the dad said, "Please don't come anymore"
For a few days I would walk past, it was my shortcut.
Then the dad opened the door, "Please come"
Their only daughter was sad, she would not smile
As soon as I entered, she laughed
Her precious dolls were handed to me. I was fed.
The poorest kid brought laughter
I was that kid.
Ta'ho'!

The King and Queen Pass By on Train

I am happy
The King and Queen will pass by on train, they say
All the boys and girls on the reservation
Will receive pants, skirts and sailor blouses.
Our parcel arrives from the Indian Agency
To the foster home where I live
There is one sailor blouse, a skirt
My heart goes flip flop.
But the fun day goes by
With no one saying, "Put your blouse on."
My heart stops.

The day is over
Gone, my longing to see the King and the Queen.
And now my foster brother has new hand-made pants
With a sailor blouse to match.

My heart goes flip flop.

For the Children

I Was a Blind Man's Eyes

After my dad died, I was taken to Oxford Junction N.S.
Where I am in care, my life not my own.
I am ten years old when a blind man comes to borrow me
What would a blind man want with me, I wondered
I was told that I had to lead him to where he wants to go.
One very early morning, we go by train to Amherst
At nine a.m. I take him from door to door
He had permission to beg, no pension yet
All day long I take him, until the return home
He pays a dollar.
I am a child, and do not know he is using me as sight
I am his eyes, he gives me direction
I am a blind man's eyes for the day until he comes again.

Imaginary Buddies

My dad dies in Millbrook Reservation, Nova Scotia, in 1942
I am ten years old, I hear the voices of an Indian Agent and others
They are discussing where to put me, finally a name I hear
Oh, not there. Just a few days ago I was in a group throwing rocks
At a man in the bushes. All the children did not like the man.
While I am thinking what to do next, somebody takes my hand
Leads me away, I follow with ease, knowing the person.
My next home place is Oxford Junction. With three native families
In September I go to school with non-natives, I try to make friends
The girls are friendly at school but not allowed to go to my home.
I ask why? No answer. The other natives live too far, no playmates.
My imaginary world begins, the maple my friend, the aspen my friend
The birds and every animal became my friend, in a while many friends.
I fed the birds and animals, hugged the trees, feeling good
And noticed that if you are good to anything, payback double
I even had names for my trees—Tom, John, Maria, like my sister
The big spruce was *Kujinu'* (Grandfather). The short balsam *Kijinu'*
Kujinu and *Kijinu* always smelled nice, so gentle, their arms touch.
And as long as I was at my playhouse I was happy.
When away sad.
My foster mother wondered why I was happy while alone at my playhouse
Her questions were not answered. One time I did, was called crazy
She inspected, nothing or nobody. Her look incredulous

To this day I like feeding birds and little animals
Once when I came home from the hospital, there were many birds
On telephone line all looking towards my house
Thank you, I told them. They still visit.

The Crow Who Spoke Mi'kmaw

In our native community which is Eskasoni
I knew a kind man, Athanasius, for short Tana's
Everybody knew he liked telling stories
So many many stories from way back in time.
So it was not a surprise when he told me
"Crows speak *Lnu*, you know"
"Do they Uncle, and how?" I replied.
"There was this *Lnu* who gave a crow his shirt,
As time passed, he asked the crow what happened to the shirt.
'*Kaq kaq aqq* (I wore it out),' replied the crow."
Today when I hear a crow caw cawing
I think of Uncle Tana's and his stories
And how I learned that they speak Mi'kmaw.

I Live in a House in Eskasoni

I live in a house in Eskasoni
Where I see this life as it passes by.
Sometimes it is good, sometimes bad.
We help when your look says so
Sometimes I feel foolish, I want to be worth something.
I never want to judge or scorn
For being part of our world
Sometimes we want to offer advice
You never listen.

In my country
I am like a left-handed compliment
Still a native of yesterday.
The wise pariah to hold at arm's length
No say!

I live in a house in Eskasoni
Looking at this life as it passes by.
Listen!
I may have something to say
Listen!
The wisest elders on my reservation never hurry
They wait, they say
Someday you will listen.

For the Children

Poor Man, Poor World

While I was writing my story
The telephone rang.
"I want to speak to Rita Joe."
"This is her speaking, Sir," I answered.
"Will you come to our school to speak?
I would appreciate it.
Whatever it is you speak about, basket weaving or what."
"I do not weave baskets, Sir.
I am a writer and speak about my culture."
"Whatever you do, speak to our children."
My phone went dead.
Poor man, poor world, I thought
The crooked world will never change.
I will though,
Putting a badge on my heart.
I will speak to his schoolchildren.
Maybe then, the next generation may not say
"Whatever it is you speak about, basket weaving or what."
Poor man, poor world.
I love his children, I am a determined Indian
I love his children and I have a heart.

Prejudice Is Something We Can Do Without

I walk into a store in town
My pockets bursting with money
My needs are like any other
For goods I want to buy in a hurry
The clerk in the store sees my face, the rugged clothes
My feet in mukluks, the headband on my brow

She has immediate ideas of the poor Indian,
The stereotype in progress
She does not know I sense ill will
So gently I turn around and walk out,
Looking for another store

One where the clerk is all smiles, even if it hurts
I have bought out the store,
My pockets empty
Prejudice is something we can do without
Accept me just as I am,
My money, and my identity

The Solid Part of One's Identity

In the expression of my tongue
I say, *Kesalin*? Do you love me?
I may say *Kesalu'l*, I love you.
Positive words are important
I do not teach hate
The solid part of one's identity
Is communication,
Exchanging words or touch
With no animosity towards another.
I have had positive experience
The past twenty-two years of writing
Trying to teach the Mi'kmaw way of life
The majority of the Mi'kmaq are peace-keeping people
They are gentle people, anxious to please
I sympathize with my people across the nation
I admire what they think should be done
But do not think a militant attitude should be used
The solid part of our identity is sharing
That is why we are here today
We are survivors.

Learning the Language

Look at the busy rivers
Where water runs over the pebbles
As if to say, "Hello, how are you? I am gone."
Or a leaf on a maple tree,
"Touch me but don't hurt."
You look but move on.

Lay on the grass
Mold your body to it, relaxing,
The spiritual in effect
And look at the sky,
The lazy roll of a cloud passing by
With pictures of dreams your mind wills
The reward of nature,
Gives you high high.

VIXEN

For the Children

Free Trade

The Mi'kmaw Indian walked from the reservation to town
Where he knew there was water
In his pocket were only pennies
With five pennies he bought one herring for bait
And nearing the water, he bit the fish
Spitting the pieces into the water
Creating the shimmering surface of oil
So mackerel will come.
Then he fished to his heart's content.
Na'pola'ji' until there were many, so many indeed
He could hardly carry them

Then he went to the nearest town
Exchanging at each house for food or loose change

Then the long walk home to the reservation
With a coarse bag of food
And loose change, jingling in pocket.

*Na'pola'ji' means
"putting fish on a forked stick"*

I Am Dancing at a Pow-Wow

I am dancing at a pow-wow
My heart exhilarated at the beat of the drums. The happiness
My happiness holds my body upright
The beat perceptive of my want.
"I dance for you my *Niskam*
I have danced since the dawn of time."
My spiritual journey, they do not recognize.
My song reaching the sky
Because I put so much declaration in the Supremacy of life
"I dance for you my *Niskam*
I dance with a joy in my heart"
This is my world.
The unity expressed in the holding of hands
Others come, they too feel the unity
The primitive expression writing the balance.
I dance.
I dance!!!!!!!!!!!

Niskam means "Creator"

Kitpu'jij (Eaglet)

A farmer had found
An egg in the home of an eagle.
He took the egg to a nest on the farm
Placing it where the hens keep warm.
In a little while, the chicks and the eaglet came
They were mothered together.
Kitpu'jij never knew different, they were the same
Finally one day *Kitpu'jij* asked
What was flying in the sky.
"Oh that is the eagle, the king of the sky!"
Kitpu'jij tried to fly but couldn't—
The king of the sky his idol.
So he tried to fly but he couldn't—
He never knew why.
Finally he died.
He never knew what it is to be king
The embrace was taken away, love from his own never there
The essence bare.
For when the circle is removed, the spirit dies.
Kitpu'jij never knew the time to come, he left
His story alive.
This is all we have, not him
He never got to be an eagle, the king of the sky.

Old Stories

There are stories told by the elderly
Of bannock baked in a bed of stone
Of birch bark fashioned into a pot
To boil meat and bone

There are tales told
Of what life was before
Of wigwam in the wood
With deerskin for a door

Fishing from canoe
Hunting in the wild
Herbs gathered for the sick
To cure and soothe

Prayers and song
Memories told to the young
When all life was *lnua'kis*

It will never be the same again
Only in our minds and elderly tales

lnua'kis means "Indian"

HAWK

For the Children

The Legend of the Sky Bear

The sky bear comes out of the den
In the spring of each year.
To be spotted and chased by seven hunters
The pursuit lasting a time.
The chase goes on through the summer
And finally in mid-autumn
The hunters overtake their prey and kill her.

The robin becomes covered with her blood
In the process tries to shake it off
Which he does, with the exception on breast.
The gore he trembles
Spattering to the earth below
And there we see autumn
The red tint on leaves
The reddest on maple.

For you see, the trees on earth
Follow the sight of trees in the sky
The sky maple received the most blood
The sky is the same as earth
Only older.

Plo'qan (overcooked porridge)

In the early seventies I was a mother to two more boys
Along with the eight of our own.
My mother-in-law called one of them *Plo'qan*
My next question was, "What is a *plo'qan*?"
She then told this story.
One time she said, a small boy was brought to Chapel Island, he was so skinny that his legs were the size of the broomstick. The old lady who took him in promised the non-native that she will cure him, the little boy was so tiny that the Mi'kmaq thought there was no way the little boy would survive. The old Indian woman cooked the rolled oats a long time, took a cloth and squeezed the broth from the well-cooked porridge. She fed the boy with a lot of patience and love. Very soon the little boy was seen very well and playing happily in the yard. He was healthy when he was picked up by his parents. Nobody knew the name of the boy, the Mi'kmaq called him *Plo'qan-jij*.
That is what she called the boy in my home. We just laughed at the time, today he is a policeman. We do not laugh anymore. When he comes to visit I get a hug like any mother, that is the part I like, the mutual admiration of mother and son. The grandma has since died, so nobody dares to call him *Plo'qan* anymore. But once in a while we remember the story, it is good.
I have told the story many times
It is a family-like legend
And if it was not for Mother-in-law
We would not know where *Plo'qan* came from.

A True Story

A Mi'kmaw boy of eleven years
Stood in the woods of Eskasoni
A cold sleet of rain had fallen
During the night in the woodlands.
He was cold and shivering
Cold and shivering in the woodlands.
He looked around unable to find
The maple tree in the woodlands.
A clean maple to strip for baskets
A clean maple in the woodlands.
He bowed his head and said a prayer
A sad prayer in the woodlands.
I cannot go home without the maple
Without the maple in the woodlands.
"*Kisu'lkw* I know you are there
I know you're there in the woodlands."
And there before him stood the maple
Ta'n mu etenukup in the woodlands.
He cut the maple without the cold
Without feeling in the woodlands.
His parents were glad there will be baskets
Baskets to sell.
And from hunger they will survive
Because of the woodlands.

*Ta'n mu etenukup
means
"where it was
not there before"*

*Kisu'lkw means
"I know you are there"*

My Heroes Were the People I Knew

The best thing one can do is to believe in one's self
That is if there is no backup
The inner glow in one's heart
Which everyone of us have had at one time or other.
That as you know is *Niskam*
He has been my major backup since I started to write
Asking for help each time, using my own words.
Today the feeling is good because of past accomplishment
Something that was done
The feeling is like climbing a ladder of happiness.
You do not want it to end but it does
Is it enough for now until another burst of inspiration?
It is you who decides, either you fall on your face
Or be a winner.
Maybe then you can do something for the community
The nation as the whole, or even your loved ones.
It helps to do what one thinks best.
The goal I set for myself was, they are going to see a good Indian
I also represent a good nation, it took a lot of effort.
My heroes were the people I knew, the elders, the people my age
The children are number one, that realization is what keeps me
Going, until such time I cannot do it anymore. *Ta'ho'*

The Indian Blacksmith

Under the shade of leafy shelter
The Micmac swings the hammer
His brow shines with sweat
From the hot embers of his forge
The twang of the heavy beat, the sound of steel
The dying craft

Eel spears, drawknives, crooked knives
And *lape'so'qn*
The aboriginal cutter of basket strips

Throughout the years he worked
Singing songs to *Niskam*
Telling of traditions he knew
Now he is gone, his questions unanswered
"Why don't they understand my culture
That I must cling to?"

He shared his talent but others cannot see.

The blacksmith is Andrew Battiste of Eskasoni
lape'so'qn means "cutter of strips"
Niskam means "God"

Migration Indian

I toss and turn all through the night
The hurting bunk-boards, the hay and quilt not enough
The alarm rings, horizon turning red
We wash, dress, eat and take buckets
Rush to the fields of blue, like rivers out of sight.
And before noon we try to reach the quota
The songs in our head unsung
We work the blueberry fields
All muscle and might.

There is a way to hold rake, wrist in motion
Or to bend your back, legs wide, moving forward
Spacing your wind, going easy, your spirit cool
In spite of the sun on back, riding your shadow.
Then noontime, cold beans or bannock
Your thoughts speed back to the field
The song in your head inspiration
The blueberry fields we work
All muscle and might.

The long walk to the blower, to clean your berries
Waiting your turn, have a cigarette.
The comparing of notes and friendly chatter.
Payday tonight, "Where's the best restaurant?"

Maybe phone home to Canada, bragging about quota
Then rest, not long, picking means money
The song in your head ready to sing
About the blueberry fields we work
All muscle and might.

We travel to find work, the migration Indian.

WOODCOCK

For the Children   *33*

Young Boys of Eskasoni

They play the drums dedication style
The longing for their culture to re-flower.
The dance not as much, only by few
The '90s art to verbalize.

The *mawiomi* the in-thing for the young
The soul-searching for esteem far-flung.
For most of the boys education-wise
The relearning of the culture exercise.

The most are anxious for the future
The uncertain age not yet in bloom.
Like all cultures looking for acknowledgement
A joy for their own a positive voice.

These are the youth on my reservation
I see each day, my inspiration.
To observe and to tell of their ambition
Soon to be men of tomorrow and assertiveness.

Mawiomi means "a gathering or a pow-wow"

Pepkijetekn (Drums)

I listened to a television program
Where I heard natives discussing suicide.
The main cause among aboriginals
Who are without jobs, the problems analyzed
Some blamed porno movies, heavy metal, negativeness
I listened, trying own way to solve the problem
Caring very much to see a solution.
Why not Lnu songs which are only a memory
The drums stored somewhere on the mind.
The positive, we play ours
The positive, we sing ours.
Re-learning is not hard, the rest falls into place
The embracing of values, all over again.
We teach, we follow, the role played
Co-existing on a spiritual trail.
Just seeing a dressed feather made my day
Consider the young
What is dear to them.
We return to the spirit what is dear
Pepkijete'ka'ti'k newtitpa'q...

Pepkijete'ka'ti'k newtitpa'q means
"We pound the drums all night long..."

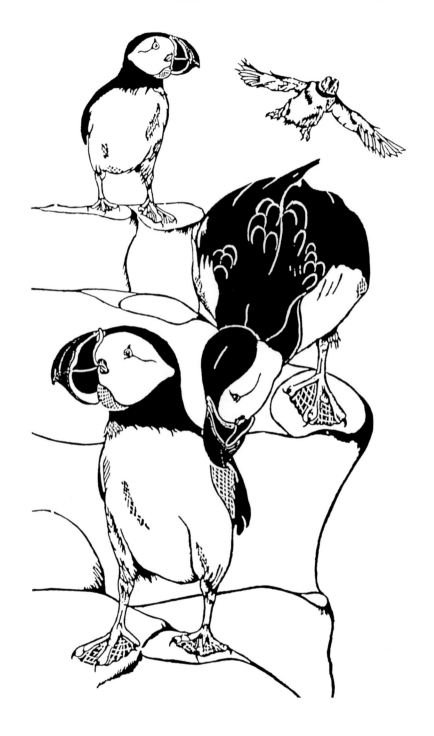

PUFFINS

Pollution

Mjikey is dirt even thinking silent
Pollution as a native bothers me.
The damage to mother earth
It is like hurting *nkij* (mother)
She has held me for sixty-six years
Her arms never tire, *kelnit* (hold)
And if damage was done a period of time
Ma'klnaql wenl (she will not hold anybody)
Mjike'k samqwan (water is dirty) we cannot drink it
Mjike'k maqmikew (dirty land) the damage is done.
Mjike'k musikisk (dirty sky) will eventually come down.
Mjike'k
Mejika'tu'kw na kinu (we dirty it)
If the thought is there at all times
Clean will be like a *jijaqamij* (shadow)
Around at all times to remind.
Na' nkij klu'sitew (my mother clean)
Na'samqwan ap waqame'tew (water be clean)
Na'musikisk musikiskewamu kutow
The sky will be blue.
Mu mjika'tukw kinu (if we do not dirty it)
Ke' pasik ankite'ten (just think about it).

EAGLES

38   **For the Children**

A Pow-wow in Shubenacadie

I enter the multi-purpose building
Where the pow-wow is held
And stand amidst the crowd
Hoping to see someone familiar, to say hello
The drummers begin to play, singing songs
That touch my heart.
A man comes out of the crowd,
And dances by me.
I am curious, "Who is he?" I ask.
A medicine man from out of the province, I am told.
I join the dance, sometimes closing my eyes,
Dancing the elderly woman dance,
My feet flat, close to earth
The song takes a long time to end
And we dance.
When I walk away from the floor
My feet are light, I walk on air
And I feel fear.
I explain the feeling to a medicine man.
"You have been in a ceremonial healing dance,"
He says, "Sit out the next one."
So I sit, amazement in my heart,
Ready to tell about the elderly woman dance.

Unamaki' (Cape Breton)

About twenty years ago
My husband Frank took the children and I
To all of Cape Breton.
The tour lasted the whole day
There was sandwiches and ice cream
Water and pop and bathrooms, sometimes woods.
I am the mother interested in land, water, sky
Our children learning from their father the beauty
Of a place we knew as *Unamaki.*
As you may realize by now the noise and hunger
Fell on the mother to minister.
Today I try to visualize what we saw
The majestic beauty still there, now seen on television.
The children grown to men and women, and their children
See what we saw yesteryear
Unamaki the beautiful.

Reminders of mind
Hold the beauty, we see again and again.

For the Children

I Thought I Knew My Country

My country, I thought I knew it.
I was looking for a smooth birch bark
In the woods, and felt so alone
A lonely feeling in my own land.
Not a movement of any creature
Not even a bird.
The added stillness like a sense of loss.

This is the place of my birth.

I looked at the mountain covered with trees
The warm breeze blowing as if to please.
This is my country, I'm thinking
A beautiful place where I was born
I know I'm supposed to know it but I don't
It is a place we live, not going anywhere

Then I kept walking deeper into the woods
There were no tracks in the snow.
The snow made a rustling sound
Something like a snapping of a twig.
Once in a while I stood still, waiting for a sound
None came, I turned back.
Finally finding what I was looking for
The bark is for framing a picture.

I Am an Indian on This Land

I am just an Indian on this land
I am sad, my culture you do not understand.
I am just an Indian to you now
You wrinkle your brow

Today you greet me with bagpipes
Today you sing your songs to me
Today we shake hands and see
How we keep good company.
Today I will tell stories
Today I play the drum and dance
Today I will say what is on my mind
For being friends is our goal.
Today I will show I am just like you
Today I will show what is true
Today I will show we can be friends
Together we agree.
Today I will tell about my race
Today I will share what is mine
Today I give you my heart
This is all we own.
Today I show.
Hello everybody, my name is Rita Joe.

Indian Residential Schools

Today on television I heard a discussion
Of residential schools across the country.
I saw a man talk about sex abuse done to him
He even had a hard time saying it.
I was in one of the schools, my daughter too
There was physical abuse where I was
Not sex but mind mistreatment.
To me there was one individual who did this
As always there are certain people who do.
The rest of the nuns were tolerable
The priest in my time a kind man.

My daughter says she didn't have it hard
But again only one person did her wrong
And upon seeing her in later years
This person hugged her and cried
My daughter knew the forgiving song.

I know for a fact people who came from schools
Have turned into productive persons.
Even women who had it hard have become nuns
And men from across the country their dreams realized.
In my case I've nobody to blame for being there
I put myself where I would receive training

The four years have given me strength
My life to this day has gained courage
I know who I am, and my people are the prize.

My Beads

I thread one bead, then the three, then one
The dividing circle, the bored piece of antler
In my mind, it is native, the creation mine
The truth on my side, the inner core
I gather to my need, to my people as well
The prayer beads as they are called
I make beautiful, so others may own.

I thread one bead, then ten, the space between
Onto the next decade as they are named.
The fifty-nine beads, the complete circle
Ending with an antler, the flat piece
The sketch of a cross on the surface.
This is my creation, my need, my fame.
You can use as a necklace, if not to my doctrine
It is native, a beautiful necklace you may wear.

It reminds who we are, our life on each bead
It reminds who we are.

I Dreamt About Seedbeds on the Wall

I dreamt about seedbeds on the wall
In the vision I take an ordinary comb,
And comb the beads off the wall.
My hand fills with them
So very shiny, beautiful.
My heart fills with admiration.
Pe'wai'ke'luk
I dream good.
The inner soul my crystal ball.

In my dream I see a conveyor belt moving
On it are my traditional values,
There are head-dresses, rattles, even the figures of my people.
I hear the drum rolling to the sky
The sad look on the face of my nation
They cry.
In the dream I want to do something, but cannot.
I become aware I am the herald, where my vision lies.

In a dream I see a hill
Where I see many children run and in happy voices.
"Where are you going?" I ask.
"*Pe'smke'way* is on the other side," they say.
I want to follow, but the inner voice cries

I am not worthy to go where they are going.
When I awaken, my writing says it all
With the children I will follow to the other side.

Wenmajita'si (I am filled with grief)

Kiskuk eksitpu'kek alasutmay
Etawey kisi wi'kiken
Etawey kisi ankita'sin
Etawey kijka' mlkikno'ti
Ma'w kitu'-kinua'tekey aq kekina'muey
We'jitutoqsɨp mu i'muann
Ankite'lmuloqop msɨt
Siaw-lukutikw nutqo'ltioq
Kisa'tutoqsɨp na.

OWLS

Today, this morning I prayed
I ask to write a little longer
I ask if I may be able to think
I ask for a small strength
I still want to show, teach.
You will find when I am gone
I thought about all of you
Continue the work, you young people
You can do it.

I Wrote, Now You Write

I want to write, but I have to wait
Until my medicine works.
The tremor then stills
The creating has to be freewill, no fear.
I used to be afraid, held back.
Do not step on toes, I was told.
But one must step on toes
If you see something incorrect.

It has been a while since I saw
But the door is still open
This time I'm asking you to help
If you see something that is not right
By all means, point it out
There will always be somebody who cares
Enough to put it right again.

We do not need the humiliation
Like in my time, even as near as in the seventies.
My children knew I was working on culture
So brought what they did not like
Attestment, it would say, rather than the negative.
The only way I knew to fight it
Write the beauty I knew and saw

For the Children *47*

Even sensed.

It has been done, now you do

When I Am Gone

When I am gone, don't cry but smile and think;
Remember the car ride we had and talked about nothing
We said something about the trees, the hills behind our homes
The church we met on Sunday, *Pe'kwam-uk-sin*, we hugged
You walked by and you stopped, we had a little chat
Nothing important, maybe about our children
Or how to cook bannock that is crisp
We drank tea together, remembering the old days.
Oh yes we have a lot in common, our husbands gone
To work and communicate with their friends.
The long wait till payday, so you have discussions about
What we need for home, our ideas put together
Women for women, men for men and our children
Who always need something

Yes, my friend
We are all the same, just ask the next person
Did she die?
Then smile, because I'll be happy
At least you asked.

Na'ta'q Ntapekiaqn (My Song Is Fading)

I'm on this path of illness
The name Parkinson's.
It is mean, it knocks you down
One hurt upon another
Until you are near paralysis.
It robs you of dignity, of tolerance
Even spirituality.
The most important when one is ill.

My song has always been of happiness
Beautiful things we enjoy on earth.
They do not matter anymore
All have lesser meaning
My body weak, the spirit down
Medication takes forty minutes to work
The illness will not break me
I promise myself, determination there
Here is my song.

MINK

Rita Joe's typewriter, as she left it.

Below, Burland Murphy stands in front of an installation of his aluminum eagle wings, now in the Lincoln Financial Field, home of the Philadelphia Eagles.

Rita Joe was born March 15, 1932, in Whycocomagh, Cape Breton Island. She was the child of Josie Gould and Annie (Googoo) Bernard, and from the age of ten she lived a hardscrabble existence, from foster home to foster home, experiences that helped her decide to admit herself to Shubenacadie Indian Residential School, a place most Mi'kmaq people had come to dread. It was a rare example of the child choosing Shubie, "to better myself," to get an education—and an example of Rita Joe's determination. Her story is told in detail in her autobiography, *Song of Rita Joe*. In 1954 she married Frank Joe, and lived most of her life in Eskasoni. And with the same determination she decided to write her story of Mi'kmaw experience. Through her personal combination of traditional Mi'kmaw spiritualism and Catholic faith she carried forward her "gentle war." Her work has appeared in anthologies and textbooks, and four books of poems: *Poems of Rita Joe*, *Song of Eskasoni*, *Lnu and Indians We're Called*, and *We are the Dreamers*. A respected Mi'kmaw elder and recipient of the Order of Canada and honorary doctorates, she died in March 2007. She worked until the end. Her last poem, unfinished, was found in her typewriter. It included the lines, "On the day I am blue, I go again to the wood where the tree is swaying, arms touching you like a friend, and the sound of the wind so alone like I am; whispers here, whispers there, come and just be my friend...."

Burland Murphy was born in 1946 and raised in Yarmouth, Nova Scotia, in the village of Pleasant Lake. "It couldn't have been a better spot for a wildlife artist to get a start. On one side of the village there were huge saltwater marshes and creeks alongside the Tusket River. On the other side there was a series of small interlocking lakes that meandered for miles through meadows and barren lands. There was so much wildlife all around me; thousands of geese would congregate on the marshes when migrating and in the spring I would join in with others in the village to dip the river for the gaspereau that came to spawn." With money from his first summer job—planting, picking and caring for strawberries—Burland bought a canoe that took him for miles on the waterways of Nova Scotia, where he could observe the wildlife. A graduate of the Nova Scotia College of Art and Design, he lives with his family in a house in the woods near Baddeck. To support his art, he has worked in the woods and at the local yacht yard, loaded pulp boats from Russia, driven the bookmobile, and spent a year on the crew that built the full-scale replica of the hydrofoil HD-4, now at the Alexander Graham Bell National Historic Site. He spent some years away from art, caring for his ailing parents. In recent years he returned to oil painting and to making metal wing sculptures, ran The Flying Squirrel, an in-home studio gallery, and now works the at-home-and-away schedule of a construction job in Fort McMurray, Alberta. Burland Murphy can be contacted at burlandmurphy@ns.sympatico.ca.

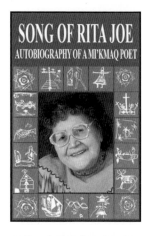

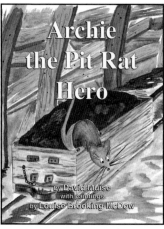
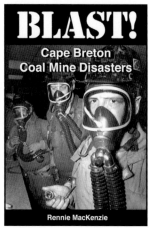